Co-occurring Disorders Series

PREVENTING RELAPSE

Revised

Katie Evans, Ph.D.

HAZELDEN

FORMERLY THE DUAL DIAGNOSIS SERIES

Hazelden
Center City, Minnesota 55012-0176

1-800-328-9000
1-651-213-4590 (Fax)
www.hazelden.org

To request permission, write to
Permissions Coordinator, Hazelden
P.O. Box 176, Center City, MN 55012-0176.
To purchase additional copies of this publication, call
1-800-328-9000 or 1-651-213-4000.

ISBN: 1-59285-005-7

Editor's note

This material was written to educate individuals about chemical dependency and mental illness. It is not intended as a substitute for professional
medical or psychiatric care.

Any stories or case studies that may be used in this material are com-
posites of many individuals. Names and details have been changed to pro-
tect identities.

Cover design by Lightbourne
Interior design by Lightbourne

For my son, Casey, and daughter, Callie.
Thank you for supporting this writing.

To all the individuals with co-existing disorders from whom I have learned much
of what I know.

CONTENTS

INTRODUCTION

You are probably reading this pamphlet because you suffer from chemical dependency and at least one coexisting psychiatric disorder. Working with a qualified professional, family and friends, and fellow members of a self-help group, you have accepted the fact that you have two diseases and have begun to work a combined program of recovery. Your program includes abstinence from mood-altering chemicals; attending Alcoholics Anonymous (AA), Narcotics Anonymous (NA), or similar self-help groups; and working the Twelve Steps.

Relapse is the return of the symptoms of one or more of your diseases after a period of improvement. Chemical dependency is a disease that is chronic, fatal, and progressive. You will always be "in recovery"—not "recovered." Because you have dual disorders, you are more at risk for relapse than someone with only one disorder. You might have a double relapse, in which symptoms of your addiction and your psychiatric disorder return.

The purpose of this pamphlet is to help you accept the possibility of relapse and to assist you in preventing it. By helping you understand more about the relapse process and by giving you some tools, you can maintain recovery from both diseases. Just by reading and thinking about what follows, you are already helping yourself.

THE RELAPSE PROCESS

Relapse is often a *process,* not an event. Understanding relapse as a process will help keep you in recovery from your co-occurring disorders.

The difficulty with viewing relapse as an event is that once you feel you have relapsed, you may begin a train of self-defeating thinking that says, *See, I'm a failure; nothing will work. I might just as well stop trying and go all the way.* Or you may think, *Maybe I don't have these problems after all and I don't need to work a program.* This sort of thinking is likely to lead you to stop working a recovery program.

It's useful for many people with dual disorders to view relapse as a process that extends over time and offers several choice points. It begins *before* you resume alcoholic drinking and addictive drug uses or *before* you experience a full-blown return of psychiatric symptoms.

Relapse typically begins with certain triggers, then proceeds to behavior we call the relapse mode, and finally turns into a full relapse. For example, you might have a series of fights with your spouse, start thinking, *I'll show him or her,* and finally go to the nearest bar. Or you might experience several sleepless nights, fatigue, and a sad mood, then think, *This antidepressant medication doesn't work,* stop taking it, and feel depressed and suicidal.

The following discussion and outline of the relapse

process on pages 6–7 may help you understand these ideas better.

Common Triggers

Some people find that they are triggered to relapse by external stressors. The stress that you can experience from major life changes, problems in living, or grief from loss can lead to the beginning of the relapse process. These stresses place demands on you that affect your body, thinking, and feelings. The relapse process for either or both diseases can be triggered by external events.

Major life changes involve such things as a household move or the birth of a child. Problems in living might involve work hassles, fights with a spouse, failure experiences, or medical problems such as chronic pain. Losses can include such things as getting fired from a job, the end of a relationship, or the death of a loved one. These stressors can trigger a return to drinking or using or a return of serious mental and emotional symptoms.

Some internal triggers that can lead to relapse are *negative emotions* such as depression, anger, and fear. Physical illness and medical problems often lead to relapse. Taking addictive prescription drugs in recovery takes considerable planning to prevent relapse.

Alcoholics Anonymous uses the word HALTS to specify negative feelings that are likely to lead to a relapse. The initials stand for Hungry, Angry, Lonely, Tired, and Sick. Cravings are another unpleasant feeling. Feeling intensely anxious, frightened, confused, or depressed because of your psychiatric illness may also lead you to seek alcohol or drugs to reduce the emotional pain or to abandon your efforts to cope with your psychiatric illness. Feeling overwhelmed may lead you to think that (a) even brief relief from the pain is worth letting go of your precious sobriety, or that (b) you won't make your psychiatric symptoms worse if you use. Guilt and shame follow this process.

Because you are recovering from both chemical dependency and a psychiatric illness, you face special challenges. What could be more of a life change than getting sober and free from symptoms of mental or emotional illness?

Working a combined program of recovery means a major shift in your life. Accepting the fact that you have two disorders is very important. By abstaining from chemicals, attending AA or similar self-help groups, and working the Twelve Steps, you will find that you will experience promise and hope. You have to develop new friendships and resolve conflicts with family members. You will also need to develop a consistent daily routine. You must combat self-defeating ways of thinking such as "nothing can help" and substitute more constructive thoughts such as "one day at a time." Negative thought patterns are referred to as "stinking thinking" in the Twelve Step program.

As a person recovering from two disorders, you will have to overcome the usual problems in living that everyone experiences and also deal with problems that may be due to your dual disorders. Perhaps a spouse is threatening to leave you or you have developed chronic medical problems or have legal charges pending because of your chemical use. Perhaps your psychiatric condition has left you with trouble thinking clearly or prone to attacks of panic or vulnerable to episodes of severe depression. Your drinking and using may have made your psychiatric disorder worse, and your psychiatric disorder may have increased the negative consequences of your drinking and using.

You may also have many losses to grieve. Perhaps you lost a promising career or a satisfying marriage. One of your biggest losses can be the loss of your drugs of choice. People who are chemically dependent come to the point when their relationship with the chemical is

THE RELAPSE PROCESS

Triggers

1. External stressors
   - major life changes such as a household move, birth of a child, new job, entering recovery
   - problems in living such as work hassles, conflict with others, failure experiences
   - losses such as a divorce, being fired from a job, medical problems, death of someone close to you

2. Negative emotions
   - depression
   - anxiety
   - anger
   - fear
   - confusion
   - loneliness

3. Unpleasant physical states such as hunger, pain, fatigue, or cravings

Relapse Mode

1. Withdrawing from others and reducing social and recreational activities

2. Stopping or reducing number of Twelve Step meetings, psychotherapy, and other therapeutic activities

3. Failing to practice and use new skills and productive thinking

4. Returning to denial and/or helpless, hopeless mind-set, or victim-stance thinking

5. Stopping medication

6. Believing chemical use is the only way to have fun or fix the problem

7. Believing chemical use won't make psychiatric symptoms worse

8. Feeling you're unique and that you don't need recovery support

> ## Relapse
>
> **1.** Return to drinking and/or using
>
> **2.** Return of major psychiatric symptoms such as suicidal thinking, panic attacks, flashbacks, hallucinations, and inability to perform tasks and responsibilities at home or work. These are also guilt and shame issues about your past and a current relapse.

the single, most important relationship in their lives. Having to say good-bye to that relationship is a major loss. In addition, people who are actively using chemicals cannot effectively grieve losses, and the beginning of sobriety can require grieving not only current losses but a backlog of many years of losses. By numbing your feelings with alcohol and other drugs, you haven't grieved many of your losses.

Psychiatric disorders also involve losses. You may have spent many months isolating yourself in your bedroom; you may have seen your family and friends withdraw in baffled anger; or you may have been unable to finish school or keep a job. A key loss can be the loss of the sense of being like everyone else and the realization that you may always need to take special care of yourself.

Having dual disorders also means experiencing hurtful, intense, or unusual feelings. You may find yourself flooded with new, uncomfortable feelings as you maintain sobriety, and you may be uncertain how to handle them. Psychiatric disorders may involve very uncomfortable and troubling emotions. This is especially true if some psychiatric symptoms return. You may begin to panic at the thought of going to an AA meeting, or you may feel so tired and sad that you don't want to work a program. You may feel confused, foggy, and unable to concentrate. You might feel suspicious of others and lose trust in your family and friends. You may also experience symptoms of withdrawal and cravings for chemicals. These kinds of feelings make it hard to live "one day at a time," to benefit completely from your new-found sobriety and from your increased mental and emotional stability.

Relapse Mode

Stressors and negative feelings can start the relapse process. What makes a difference is how you respond to these stressors. If you respond in old, unproductive ways and stop working a combined program, you may be in relapse mode and at high risk for a relapse. If so, you may show a number of danger signals. You may begin to avoid others and stop going to AA or NA meetings. You may discontinue your medication or stop attending therapy. You may avoid social and recreational activities. You may begin to deny that you have dual disorders, make excuses for why you don't need to work a recovery program, or convince yourself that your program isn't working. When you are in this mode, you are entering relapse even if you have not yet used drugs or alcohol or not yet experienced a deterioration in your mental and emotional condition.

Some beliefs represent important danger signals. The belief in a chemical "fix" is one such belief. An example of this is the notion that life was more fun and exciting during the good old days of drinking and using. Telling war stories that highlight the fun and thrills of those times and that even exaggerate and romanticize those episodes are a setup for relapse. A more subtle form of this thinking is the belief that a drink would make you feel better or that a pill would ease the pain. Another dangerous belief is that drinking and using won't make your psychiatric disorder worse. An unstable brain chemistry is not helped by adding mood-altering chemicals.

John's Story

John was discharged from a brief stay at a psychiatric hospital following a suicide attempt. His condition had recently been diagnosed as manic depression, and he had been put on the medication lithium carbonate. The staff at the hospital were very helpful in explaining to John that lithium was like a body salt and would stabilize a chemical imbalance in his system. In addition, John finally came to accept that he was an alcoholic and a drug addict. He had begun attending AA and NA meetings, and about sixty days after he left the hospital, he began work on his Fourth Step, taking a self-inventory. As John listed all his resentments and did a sexual inventory, he became consumed with guilt. As his guilt increased, so did his depression. John began to doubt his ability to stay sober and also his desire to stay sober. John began to remember the "good times" he used to have before he got sober. John was in relapse mode.

Elizabeth's Story

Elizabeth began drinking at age seven. She learned very early that drinking helped her numb herself when her stepfather would visit her room at night. The "touching" began when she was seven; by the time she was nine, her stepfather was having intercourse with her. By age ten, Elizabeth was a full-blown alcoholic. At age twelve, she was sent to live with her mother's sister. While Elizabeth's mother believed her daughter's stories of abuse, she blamed her, insisting that Elizabeth had led her stepfather on. At age eighteen, Elizabeth went to her first AA meeting, where she found the unconditional love and support she had sought all her life. Elizabeth earned a thirty-day medallion, then relapsed. On her third try at more than thirty days of sobriety, Elizabeth noticed that she was thinking, *I'm going to fail again* and began doubting that the program would work for her. She began isolating herself. Her loneliness increased. In an attempt to deal with her loneliness, Elizabeth went to an old drinking buddy's house. Elizabeth drank coffee while her friend drank wine. The two talked for three hours about good times they had shared while partying in the past. That night, as she tried to sleep, Elizabeth felt overwhelmed with anger, sadness, and fear. She felt flooded with pain, guilt, and despair. She saw her stepfather's face and felt frightened and alone. Elizabeth began thinking, *I just can't handle this anymore.* Elizabeth was in relapse mode.

The Alternative

In contrast, if you respond in new, productive ways to your triggers, you are unlikely to relapse. Working a good program can give you the support and tools necessary to handle stress and deal with negative feelings. Even if you are in relapse mode, you can take immediate, positive action to avoid a full relapse. Calling your sponsor, attending more meetings, taking your medication, going to therapy, and practicing constructive, honest thinking will help you move out of relapse mode. The important message is that you can learn to recognize signs of relapse, and, with willingness, you can do something about it.

TWO

TOOLS FOR PREVENTING RELAPSE

The single best strategy for preventing a relapse is to work an effective and complete recovery program for both your addiction and your psychiatric disorder. Your recovery program will give you the support, attitudes, and skills to handle stressful situations and combat negative thinking and emotions.

A Daily Schedule

A useful tool for working a solid program is to develop and use a *daily schedule.* It will provide you with a structure for maintaining a recovery program and for ensuring a healthy balance of work, play, and relationships in your life. You may want to write down an hour-by-hour daily schedule that outlines your day and week, including not only your work and play activities but also your self-care, such as therapy appointments, medication times, and Twelve Step meetings. Be sure to include time to eat properly, to exercise, and to pursue a hobby or take some time for yourself. You don't have to account for every minute, but try to avoid large blocks of empty time, especially if these were times that you structured in the past by drinking and using. Your family, friends, sponsor, or therapist can help you with this task. Sticking to this schedule as much as possible will help you do what you need to do to promote your recovery. Failure to follow through on many of your planned activities will also serve as a cue that you may be in relapse mode and that problem solving and positive action are in order. Appendix A, on pages 19–20, offers a sample weekly schedule you can use.

John's Solution

John called his sponsor and told him, "I don't think I can stay sober." John's sponsor came over and did a Fifth Step with him (in which John admitted to his sponsor "the exact nature" of his wrongs). By reviewing and discussing his Fourth Step (where John had taken "a searching and fearless moral inventory" of himself), John discovered he wasn't so bad after all. One thing John's sponsor noticed was that John seemed to focus on how "bad" he was when he had too much free time. So John and his sponsor worked out a daily schedule to keep John busy and focused on pro-recovery attitudes. John had prevented relapse mode from turning into a relapse. He worked at forming positive thoughts rather than negative self-defeating thinking, and his attitude switched from self-pity to gratitude.

Fail-Safe Cards

Another effective strategy is to develop *fail-safe cards*. This involves identifying situations that trigger old thoughts and behaviors that lead to cravings for alcohol and other drugs. Then, you can find new helpful responses that have a good chance of getting you out of relapse mode. Write out both your risky situations and your preventive actions on index cards. Carry them with you in your pocket or purse, or place them where you're likely to see them regularly, such as your bedroom mirror. If you begin to experience danger signals, fail-safe cards can prompt you to take positive action. Include names and phone numbers of people to call.

Take advantage of the fact that you are an expert on yourself. Recall the sequence of events in the past that has led to drinking and using and to an intensification of your psychiatric symptoms. Review the previous section, "The Relapse Process" (pages 3–10), and the chart of the same name (pages 6–7) for additional ideas, or imagine what situations might be risky for you. Perhaps having a fight with a spouse is a situation that triggers the urge to use drugs or alcohol. Perhaps several sleepless nights signal a possible return to your psychiatric disorder.

The next step is to think of several concrete, specific steps that you can take to avoid a relapse. Examples might include going to an AA meeting, calling your sponsor or physician to discuss an increase in psychiatric symptoms, or reading the AA Big Book. Make one card for relapse of your co-occurring disorders, another for drinking and using, and one for your psychiatric disorder.

Each fail-safe card should include the following: (1) a risky situation, (2) a trigger, and (3) a helpful solution. Don't try to be fancy but do try to be specific and concrete. Focus on a few key situations that pertain to you (and don't try to "fail-safe" everything). For example, suppose a person has a history of chronic pain and of prescription drug addiction. The fail-safe card might look like this:

Front of Card

Risky situation—
physical illness, chronic back pain

Trigger—
going to a doctor and thinking about asking for pain medication

> **Back of Card**
>
> Solutions:
> 1. Tell my doctor I'm an addict and can't take pain medication.
> 2. Ask my sponsor to go to the doctor with me.
> 3. Ask for a referral for physical therapy, relaxation training, or other nonaddictive ways to help with the pain.

Or suppose a person has a history of major depression and alcoholism. Then the fail-safe card might look like this:

> **Front of Card**
>
> *Risky situation—*
> failure experience
>
> *Trigger—*
> when my mother tells me I'm stupid and will never amount to anything

> **Back of Card**
>
> Solutions:
> 1. Call my sponsor at (phone number).
> 2. Go to a meeting and talk about my feelings.
> 3. Make a list of my assets and accomplishments and review it.

Appendix B, on pages 21–22, contains a fail-safe worksheet that you may find useful for developing your fail-safe cards.

Elizabeth's Solution

Elizabeth had decided that no matter what, this time she was not going to get drunk or high. She felt her only other option was suicide. Elizabeth tore her house apart looking for the perfect means to end her own life. She was startled by the sound of her telephone. It was her AA sponsor, Karen, who had experienced a strong urge to call. Elizabeth told Karen that she wanted to die. Karen came over and spent the night with Elizabeth. The next day, Elizabeth sat in a psychologist's office telling her secret about her childhood abuse for the first time. The therapist developed a set of fail-safe cards with Elizabeth. One set was to keep her "safe" when the memories returned. The other was to ensure her sobriety. Elizabeth identified her triggers and new behaviors to cope with the triggers effectively. She stayed sober and stayed in therapy, and gradually she was able to discard the pain and wreckage of her past while maintaining her sobriety.

Fear underlies many types of relapse. A favorite acronym of mine defines FEAR as: False Evidence Appearing Real.

CONCLUSION

Many people with chronic illnesses are vulnerable to relapse. Keeping a daily schedule and creating fail-safe cards can keep you from a relapse in either of your disorders. If you are someone who is prone to relapse, it doesn't mean that you are "bad" or not working a program; it may mean that your special problems require special solutions. I hope this pamphlet can help you prevent a relapse and continue your recovery.

Summary

Remember this pamphlet's key points:

1. People with a psychiatric disorder who are also chemically dependent have to face the possibility of relapse of either or both of their diseases.

2. Relapse is a process with warning signals that can provide an opportunity to prevent a relapse.

3. A daily schedule and fail-safe cards are two useful tools for continuing in recovery.

4. Most important for dual recovery is the HOW in how it works: Honesty, Openness, Willingness.

A Final Note

Suppose that despite your best intentions and efforts you do relapse. Remember that self-criticism, guilt, and shame can pull you further into the relapse process. Realize that you have only made a mistake, that you can learn from this mistake, and that you can recommit to working a recovery program one day at a time.

DAILY SCHEDULE

Use the chart on the next page as a model to develop your daily schedule one week at a time. Block out the times for specific activities and jot down the name of the activity in that block. Include your work, play, and interpersonal activities as well as your recovery activities. You need not account for every minute, but avoid large blocks of unscheduled time. Should this happen, plan a pro-recovery activity for that time. Review your plan daily and make adjustments as necessary.

Daily Schedule

Week of _____

	Sun.	Mon.	Tues.	Wed.	Thurs.	Fri.	Sat.
AM 8							
9							
10							
11							
12							
PM 1							
2							
3							
4							
5							
6							
7							
8							
9							
10							
11							

FAIL-SAFE WORKSHEET

While the worksheet on page 22 is too small to write in, carry out these instructions using a full-size sheet of paper.

1. Review the risky situations in column 1 and check two or three that are especially risky for you.

2. In column 2 write out a detailed description of the trigger(s) for each risky situation you selected.

3. Then in column 3 write two or three solutions for each trigger.

4. Transfer the entries in the columns to your fail-safe cards.

Risky Situation	Trigger	Possible Solutions
Different living situation		
New job or promotion		
New romantic relationship		
Work or school hassles		
Being around anti-recovery people		
Conflict with others		
Financial troubles		
Legal problems		
Failure experiences		
Schedule too busy		
Divorce or separation		
Death of loved one		
Loss of job		
Loss of physical health		
Depression		
Anger		
Anxiety		
Fear		
Confusion		
Loneliness		
Unpleasant physical states like hunger, fatigue, pain, cravings		
Other		

Hazelden Foundation, a national nonprofit organization founded in 1949, helps people reclaim their lives from the disease of addiction. Built on decades of knowledge and experience, Hazelden's comprehensive approach to addiction addresses the full range of individual, family, and professional needs, including addiction treatment and continuing care services for youth and adults, publishing, research, higher learning, public education, and advocacy.

A life of recovery is lived "one day at a time." Hazelden publications, both educational and inspirational, support and strengthen lifelong recovery. In 1954, Hazelden published *Twenty-Four Hours a Day,* the first daily meditation book for recovering alcoholics, and Hazelden continues to publish works to inspire and guide individuals in treatment and recovery, and their loved ones. Professionals who work to prevent and treat addiction also turn to Hazelden for evidence-based curricula, informational materials, and videos for use in schools, treatment programs, and correctional programs.

Through published works, Hazelden extends the reach of hope, encouragement, help, and support to individuals, families, and communities affected by addiction and related issues.

For questions about Hazelden publications,
please call **800-328-9000**
or visit us online at **hazelden.org/bookstore.**

The Co-occurring Disorders Series is the definitive resource on chemical addiction combined with psychiatric illnesses. Formerly titled the Dual Diagnosis Series, it has been updated with new findings, redesigned for greater readability, and expanded with additional materials.

This informative pamphlet is a useful tool for people in all stages of recovery. Descriptions, definitions, and personal stories will help you recognize co-occurring disorders and begin your recovery program.

Katie Evans, Ph.D., NCACII, CADCII, has a doctoral degree in clinical psychology and is a board-certified alcohol and drug counselor. She is an international workshop presenter, staff trainer, and program consultant. She has written books, booklets, and other client material on the topic of co-occurring disorders.

OTHER RESOURCES ON THIS SUBJECT:
#2162 Preventing Relapse workbook
#2490 Preventing Relapse DVD

HazeLDeN

15251 Pleasant Valley Road
Center City, MN 55012-0176

1-800-328-9000
(Toll Free U.S. and Canada)
1-651-213-4000
(Outside the U.S. and Canada)
1-651-213-4590 (Fax)
www.hazelden.org

Order No. 2163

ISBN 978-1-59285-005-1

9 781592 850051

90000